ILLUSTRATIONS
contain clues to help your child complete the activities. Look for the clues together and encourage your child to count out loud as they point

NUMBER TRACK
can be used to help your ch___ ___
number is greater or less than
move their finger left on th
number to the second, then th
if they have to move their fi
good practice for your child t

G000160583

HOW MANY?
Ask your child to count how many items there are and to write the appropriate numerals in the boxes.

After that night, the shoemaker never saw the elves again. But from then on, he had good luck in all that he did.

How many cakes? ☐

How many coins? ☐

How many flowers? ☐

How many cats? ☐

How many people? ☐

How many spots? ☐

How many bows? ☐

How many shoes? ☐

About the consultant
Experienced Key Stage 1 and Key Stage 2 teacher Caroline Clissold is passionate about raising standards in mathematics teaching in primary schools. She was a consultant and regional co-ordinator for the National Centre for Excellence in the Teaching of Mathematics, delivers in-service training for a specialist mathematics education publisher, supports teaching and learning in various schools, and has guest lectured at a number of London universities. Her aim is to increase children's enjoyment of mathematics, helping them to see purpose in their learning. She strongly believes in a creative approach to teaching so that children can use and apply maths skills in meaningful contexts.

___tched into beautiful
to the night.

r symbols in the circles?

7 ◯ 9

SQUARE BOXES are for numbers; **ROUND BOXES** are for symbols

QUESTIONS FROM THE CHARACTERS encourage your child to engage with the story and illustrations, and provide extra activities

TICKS for your child to trace when they complete each spread provide an extra sense of achievement

Well done! ✓

15

Is your pen wipe-clean? Test it here:

1 2 3

NUMBERS ONE AND TWO
Ask your child to point to all the things on the table that show one. Help them to write the correct symbol in the circle. Do the same on the opposite page for the number two. Help them to write the correct numbers in the boxes.

Once upon a time there was a poor shoemaker. There came a day when he could only buy enough leather to make one more pair of shoes.

Can you draw a circle around each of the things on this table that show one?

> means *more than*
< means *less than*

Can you write the **correct symbol** in the circle?

1 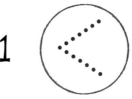 2

That night, he cut the leather to the right size and then went to bed. In the morning, he was amazed to find the shoes finished – they were beautiful!

How can we make 2?

Can you draw a circle around each of the things on this table that show two?

Can you write the **correct symbols** in the circles?

3   >   2   2   <   4

Well done!

NUMBER THREE
Ask your child to point to all the things that show three. Help them to write the correct numbers in the boxes. Then help them to write the correct symbols in the circles.

The shoemaker put the shoes in the shop window. At once a customer came in and bought them. She paid a very good price.

How can we make 3?

With the money, the shoemaker bought enough leather to make two more pairs of shoes.

Can you write the **correct symbols** in the circles?

3 ◯ 5   3 ◯ 2

Well done!

The shoemaker woke in the morning to find the two pairs of shoes already made – and every bit as fine as the first pair. Customers were waiting outside – they had heard about the beautiful shoes.

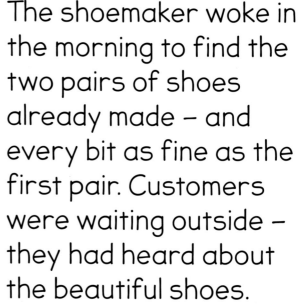

How can we make 4?

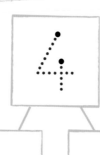

Can you draw a circle around each of the things that show four?

8

The two new pairs sold quickly, and the shoemaker bought enough leather to make four more pairs of shoes.

Can you write the **correct symbols** in the circles?

4 ◯ 2   4 ◯ 5

Well done!

9

The next day, four pairs of shoes were ready and waiting. And so it went on, day after day.

How can we make 5?

1 2 3 4 5 6 7 8 9 10

Can you write the **correct symbols** in the circles?

5 ◯ 6

5 ◯ 1

Well done!

That night, the shoemaker decided to find out who was helping him. He hid, and waited.

Can you draw a circle around each of the things that show six on this page?

Can you write the **correct symbols** in the circles?

6 ◯ 3   6 ◯ 8

12

1 2 3 4 5 6 7 8 9 10

How can we make 6?

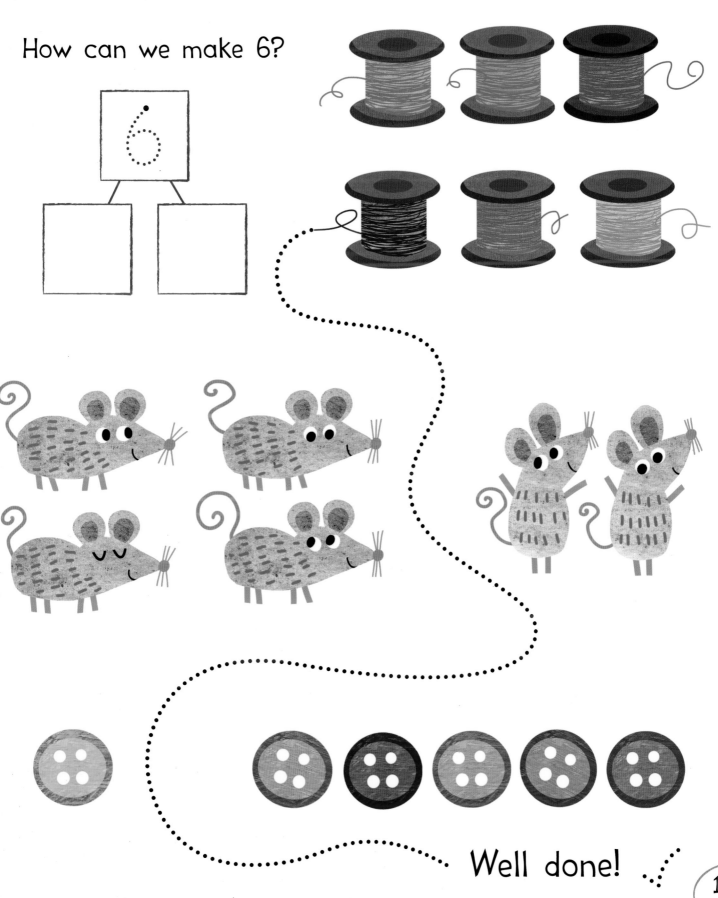

6

Well done!

At midnight, two little elves crept in. They were dressed all in rags. As the shoemaker watched, they began to stitch, sew, and hammer.

How can we make 7?

1 2 3 4 5 6 7 8 9 10

When all the leather was stitched into beautiful shoes the elves ran away into the night.

Can you write the **correct symbols** in the circles?

7 ◯ 3   7 ◯ 9

Can you draw a circle around each of the things that show seven?

Well done! ✓

15

The shoemaker thought he must find a way to thank the elves for their help. So in the morning he set to work, making new little clothes, and tiny pairs of shoes.

Can you draw a circle around each of the things on the table that show eight?

Can you write the **correct symbols** in the circles?

8 ◯ 10   8 ◯ 3

1 2 3 4 5 6 7 8 9 10

How can we make 8?

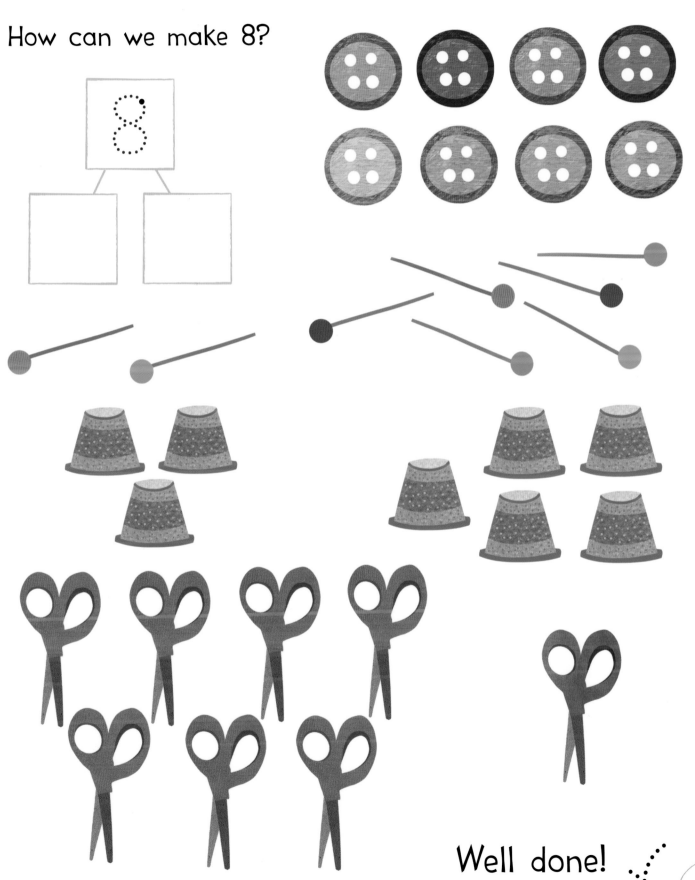

Well done!

A few nights later, when everything was ready, the shoemaker laid the presents out on his workbench and hid.

How can we make 9?

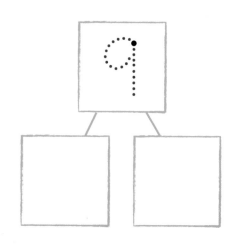

Can you draw a circle around each of the things that show nine?

18

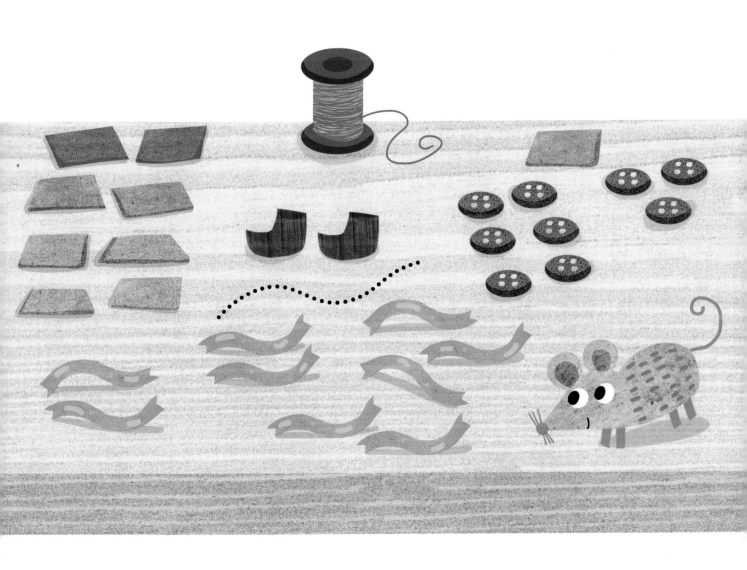

Can you write the **correct symbols** in the circles?

9 ◯ 4   9 ◯ 10

Well done! ✓

When the elves saw the clothes they put them on at once, and danced about with glee. Then they ran away, out of the shop into the night.

How can we make 10?

1 2 3 4 5 6 7 8 9 10

Can you write the correct symbols in the circles?

10 ◯ 12   10 ◯ 4

Can you draw a circle around each of the things that show ten?

Well done!

HOW MANY?
Ask your child to count how many items there are and to write the appropriate numerals in the boxes.

After that night, the shoemaker never saw the elves again. But from then on, he had good luck in all that he did.

How many **cakes?**

How many **coins?**

How many **flowers?**

How many **cats?**

22